Independent Schools
Examinations Board

GEOGRAPHY PRACTICE EXERCISES
13+

Belinda Froud-Yannic

Independent Schools
Examinations Board

www.galorepark.co.uk

GALORE PARK

Published by ISEB Publications, an imprint of Galore Park Publishing Ltd
19/21 Sayers Lane, Tenterden, Kent TN30 6BW
www.galorepark.co.uk

Design and typesetting Typetechnique
Printed by L.E.G.O. SpA, Italy
ISBN 978 1 907047 67 1

First published 2011

Details of other ISEB Revision Guides for Common Entrance, examination
papers and Galore Park publications are available at www.galorepark.co.uk

Contents

Introduction

I hope you find this book a useful tool for improving your marks in Geography. Your teacher may ask you to answer some of the questions in class or as homework. You could also try some yourself as revision before your examination.

The book is split into the different topic areas covered in the syllabus. At the end of the book there is some advice on the coursework which you prepare as part of your examination.

Questions to help you revise the Ordnance Survey part of your examination can be found in *Mapwork Practice Exercises* available from Galore Park.

If the Common Entrance examination has three sections, one which tests Ordnance Survey skills, one which tests the five themes and one which tests your knowledge of global location.

It would be a good idea to use these practice questions and the *Mapwork Practice Exercises* in combination with the *Geography ISEB Revision Guide*. You could revise a chapter from the guide and then test yourself using the questions in this book. Remember to check your answers in the *Answer Book*.

If you find that you are getting some questions wrong, ask your teacher to explain the answer to you.

Here are a few handy hints to help you breeze through the examinations!

- Always read the questions carefully, underlining, circling or highlighting key words or phrases.

- Do not leave blanks. If you do not know the answer take an educated guess. Wrong answers do not lose marks.

- Make sure that all diagrams are clearly annotated (labelled).

- Look carefully at the resources given e.g. maps, graphs etc; they will normally help you answer the question.

- Look at the number of marks available in order to assess how much to write.

- Make sure you answer the question which has been set!

- Include impressive **geographical terms** whenever possible.

I do wish you all the best of luck in all of your examinations and remember that you can be a top geographer!

Belinda Froud-Yannic

2011

Using this book

The book has been designed for use by students, under the guidance of a teacher or parent, as a resource for recall of knowledge.

Worksheets are available to assist with some questions and are indicated by a $\boxed{6}$ with the relevant number. These are available from www.geographyexercises.co.uk

Belinda Froud-Yannic
2011

1. Rivers and coasts

1.1 Which option best completes each of the following sentences?

(a) Traction is .... (1)

a method of erosion	a method of transportation
a feature of erosion	a method of coastal defence

(b) Load is .... (1)

all the material that a river carries	the speed of the water
the start of a river	the power of a wave

(c) Abrasion is .... (1)

pieces of load hitting each other	the water moving against the bank
acid in river water	load scraping against the bed and bank

(d) Fetch is .... (1)

the length of a river	the uninterrupted distance a wave travels
the speed at which a river flows	a type of weathering

(e) An arch is .... (1)

a feature of erosion	a feature of deposition
a river feature	part of a meander

(f) A river cliff is .... (1)

the inside bend of a meander	the outside bend of a meander
a feature of deposition	found at the source of a river

(g) Suspension is .... (1)

a method of erosion	fine load being carried in the flow
the overhang on a river cliff	fine load dissolved in the water

(h) Water flows faster .... (1)

on the inside of a bend of a river	on the outside of a bend in a river
at the river beach	at the slip off slope

(i) Deposition occurs .... (1)

on the river cliff	at a waterfall
on the river beach	on the outside bend of a river

(j) Longshore drift helps to form a .... (1)

spit	stump
meander	cave

1.2 Describe **three** of the processes below.

hydraulic action   **saltation**
   corrosion   **deposition**   (6)

1.3 (a) Explain the difference between weathering and erosion.   (2)

(b) Give an example of each of these processes.   (2)

1.4 Draw a diagram with detailed labels to explain how a waterfall is formed.   (5)

1.5 (a) Using the following labels annotate a copy of the photograph shown below.   (4)

shallow water	river beach
river cliff	undercutting

(b) On the copy of the photograph draw a red dotted line to show the
fastest flowing water.   (1)

1.6 Look at the OS map on the inside back cover and using map evidence only locate **two** river landforms. Copy and complete the following table, giving the four figured grid reference for each landform and stating whether the process of erosion or deposition or both processes are occurring at each location. (6)

River landform	Grid square	Process

1.7 Look at the photo below and describe how humans have interfered with the natural physical processes on the beach. (3)

1.8 Look at the OS map on the inside back cover and the sketch map below.

On a copy of the sketch map shown below, **mark** and **label** one area of coastal deposition. (2)

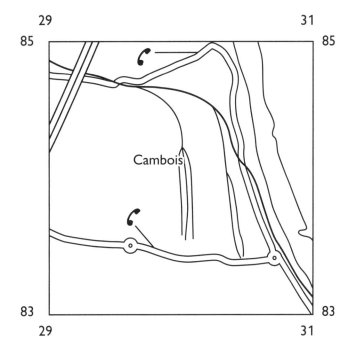

1.9   Copy the table below and match the following words to the appropriate type
      of weathering.   (4)

limestone	desert	mountain	chalk hills

Type of weathering	
onion-skin weathering	
freeze-thaw weathering	
biological weathering	
chemical weathering	

1.10 Copy and complete the following sentences by choosing the correct words from the
      box below.

impermeable	confluence	onion-skin	tributary
v-shaped valley	source	erosion	traction
brook	stump	weathering	swash
scree	permeable	freeze-thaw	arch
wave-cut platform	floodplain	drainage basin	mouth

(a) Where a river begins is known as the . . . . (1)

(b) The point where two rivers meet is called a . . . . (1)

(c) The area drained by a river and its tributaries is called a . . . . (1)

(d) The flat area either side of a river, which is regularly flooded, is called a . . . . (1)

(e) A small river that flows into a large river is called a . . . . (1)

(f) Rock and soil that does not allow water to pass through it is known as . . . . (1)

(g) When a stack is weathered and eroded it could turn into a . . . . (1)

(h) . . . . weathering is most likely to occur in a desert. (1)

(i) The breakdown of rock by weather, plants and animals is known as . . . . (1)

(j) The movement of a wave up the beach is known as . . . . (1)

(k) Loose, broken up rock is known as . . . . (1)

1.11   The diagram below shows a waterfall.

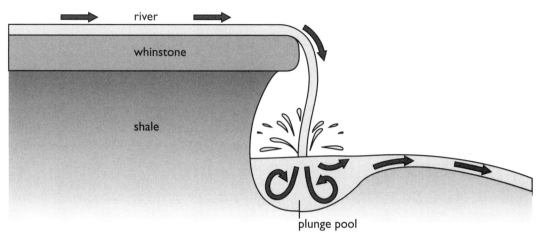

(a) Which rock is harder, whinstone or shale?   (1)

(b) How can you tell?   (2)

(c) Why is the plunge pool deeper than the river further downstream?   (3)

(d) Draw a diagram to show what you think the waterfall will look like in
    500 years' time.   (1)

(e) What processes happen to make the waterfall look like this?   (3)

1.12   (a) Explain where and why a river deposits its load.   (2)

       (b) Name a feature created by river deposition.   (1)

1.13   (a) Draw a diagram with detailed labels to explain the process of longshore drift.   (4)

       (b) Name a feature formed by longshore drift.   (1)

       (c) Draw a diagram with detailed labels to explain how this feature is formed.   (6)

1.14   (a) The diagram below shows a type of weathering. What is this process called?   (1)

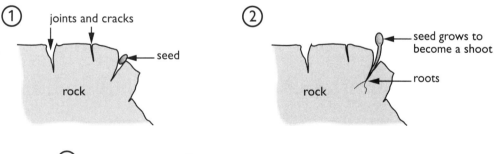

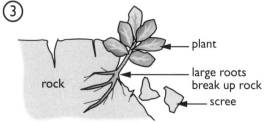

(b) Look at the photo below. What type of weathering is most likely to have occurred on these rocks? (1)

(c) Explain how this type of weathering breaks up rock. (3)

1.15 Copy the table below and put the following landforms into the correct columns to show which process has formed them. (6)

| arch | stump | beach | waterfall | spit | floodplain |

Erosion	Deposition

1.16 The diagram below shows a river. Draw a sketch section of the meander from X to Y. (2)

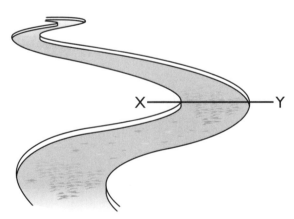

Label the following on your sketch section. (6)

| river cliff | river beach | deep water | shallow water |
| undercutting | overhang | | |

1.17 Draw a diagram with detailed labels to show how an arch is formed. On the same diagram show what may happen to the arch in the future. (6)

1.18 For each of the following, state whether it is a **cause** or an **effect** of river flooding.

(a) Heavy monsoon rainfall. (1)

(b) Steep slopes. (1)

(c) Communications destroyed. (1)

(d) Every spring the rivers carry large volumes of water from the thawing snow in the Himalayas. (1)

(e) Towns have been built on the floodplain. (1)

(f) The water spreads disease. (1)

(g) Trees have been cut down for firewood and to make space for agriculture. (1)

1.19 (a) Describe the causes of flooding in an area you have studied. (4)

(b) Humans are often badly affected by river floods. Referring to the photograph above, and your own knowledge, describe the possible impact of flooding on:

(i) the environment (3)

(ii) the people in the area (3)

(c) What can humans do to try and prevent flooding? (4)

1.20 Copy and complete the following sentences by choosing the correct word from the box below.

erosion	deposition	transportation	urbanisation
deforestation	impermeable clay soil	river cliff	waterfall
slip-off slope	chemical	biological	physical

(a) The major process responsible for the formation of a stack and a waterfall is . . . (1)

(b) The major process responsible for the formation of a beach and floodplain is . . . (1)

(c) . . . . is a physical cause of flooding. (1)

(d) A . . . . is a feature of deposition. (1)

(e) . . . . weathering is likely to be caused by
a change of temperature. (1)

1.21 (a) Match the labels below to the appropriate diagram to indicate where in
the course of the river the load would be of each size and shape. (3)

upper course of the river (near the source)
middle course
lower course of the river (near the mouth)

(i) ①

(ii) ②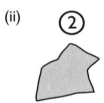

(iii) ③

(b) Explain why a river's load changes size and shape as it flows from
source to mouth. (2)

1.22 (a) Describe and explain the processes that occur on the inside edge of a meander. (3)

(b) Describe and explain the processes that occur on the outside edge of a meander. (3)

1.23 (a) On a copy of the diagram of a river below, use a dotted line to show the fastest flowing current in the river. (1)

(b) Shade yellow places where deposition would occur and red at places where erosion would occur. (2)

2. Weather and climate

2.1   Which option best completes each of the following sentences?

(a)   Relief rainfall occurs . . . . (1)

in mountainous areas	in desert areas
in the east of England	in rainforests

(b)   Convectional rainfall occurs . . . . (1)

in rainforests every day	in Scotland in winter
in rainforests once a month	in Scotland in summer

(c)   Frontal rainfall occurs . . . . (1)

when two warm air masses meet
when a cold air mass rises over a warm air mass
when two cold air masses meet
when a warm air mass rises over a cold air mass

(d)   Precipitation is . . . . (1)

the movement of water through soil	when water vapour turns to liquid
when water turns to vapour	rain, snow, hail or sleet

(e)   Interception is . . . . (1)

the movement of water through soil
when rain hits a roof or tree before landing
the release of water vapour from trees
when water flows over the ground

(f)   Infiltration is . . . . (1)

when water turns to vapour
the vertical movement of water through soil
when water vapour turns to liquid
when water flows over the ground

(g)   Condensation occurs when . . . . (1)

water turns to vapour
heating turns water vapour into a liquid
water vapour is released from trees
cooling turns water vapour into a liquid

(h) Altitude is . . . . (1)

the height above sea level	the direction something is facing
the shape of the land	a type of precipitation

(i) In the UK we experience a rain shadow effect . . . . (1)

where there is most rainfall	in the west of England
in the east of England	in the rainforest

(j) Aspect is . . . . (1)

the direction something is facing	the side of a hill
a place facing the Sun	the distance something is from the sea

2.2   The diagram below shows a sketch section of High House Farm in Devon, England.

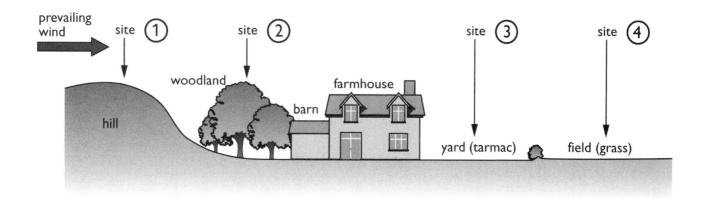

(a) The farmer is interested in measuring the weather. Where would be the
best place for him to place his Stevenson screen?   (1)

(b) In the daytime, in the summer, which site would be the warmest?   (1)

(c) Why would this site be the warmest?   (1)

(d) Which site would be the windiest?   (1)

(e) Why would this site be the windiest?   (1)

(f) Which site would be the coldest?   (1)

(g) Why would this site be the coldest?   (1)

2.3 On a copy of the diagram of relief rainfall below add the following labels in the correct places. (5)

| condensation | evaporation | precipitation | rain shadow | air cools |

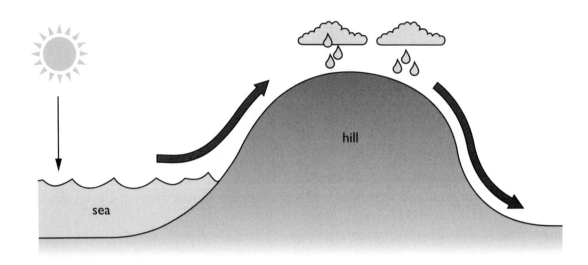

2.4 Describe and explain how **two** of the following affect the climate of the British Isles.

altitude **latitude** **distance from the sea** (4)

2.5 Draw a diagram with detailed labels to explain why convectional rainfall occurs. (5)

2.6 Define the following terms:

(a) humidity (1)

(b) transpiration (1)

(c) prevailing wind (1)

(d) surface run-off (1)

2.7 (a) What is a microclimate? (1)

(b) Name three factors that affect a microclimate. (3)

(c) Look at grid square **1985** on the OS map on the inside back cover and describe how the microclimate in this square could be different to the climate in the surrounding area. (3)

(d) Why would the microclimate in this square be different to the climate in the surrounding area? (3)

2.8   Copy and complete the following sentences by choosing the correct words from the box below.

| convectional | cools | relief | horizontal | warms |
| east | vertical | west | cooler | warmer |

(a)   . . . . rainfall could occur in the summer in London.   (1)

(b)   The . . . . of England has more rainfall than the east.   (1)

(c)   The . . . . movement of water though soil is known
       as infiltration.   (1)

(d)   The Gulf Stream (North Atlantic Drift) . . . .
       the west of the British Isles in the winter.   (1)

(e)   In the winter places near to the sea are . . . .
       than places inland.   (1)

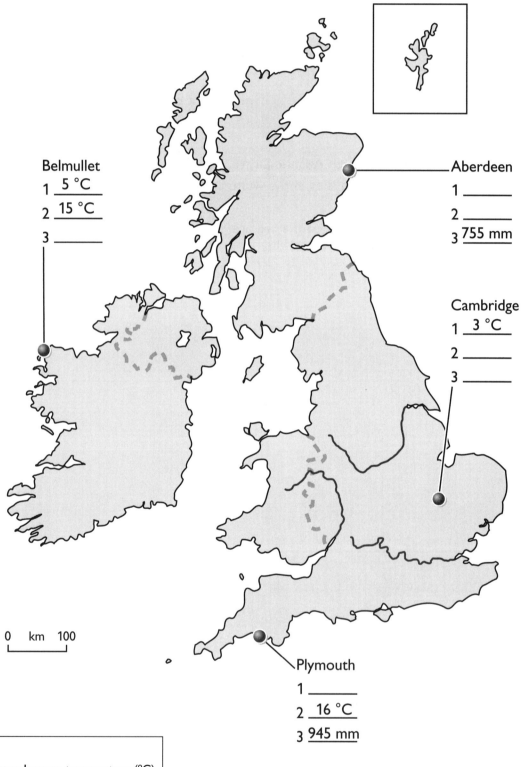

2.9   Study the map below. On a copy of the map insert the missing climate data.   (6)

6

Missing climate data

1132 mm   17°C   3°C   6°C   12°C   557mm

Belmullet
1 _5 °C_
2 _15 °C_
3 _____

Aberdeen
1 _____
2 _____
3 _755 mm_

Cambridge
1 _3 °C_
2 _____
3 _____

Plymouth
1 _____
2 _16 °C_
3 _945 mm_

0   km   100

Key
1. Average January temperature (°C)
2. Average July temperature (°C)
3. Annual rainfall total (mm)

14

2.10 (a) In the UK from which direction is the prevailing wind? (1)

(b) How does the prevailing wind influence the climate of the British Isles? (4)

2.11 Look at the OS map on the inside back cover and find grid squares 2991 and 1890. Where would you expect to record the higher daytime temperature and why? (2)

2.12 Draw a well-labelled diagram to show why frontal rainfall occurs. (5)

2.13 Explain the difference between weather and climate. (2)

2.14 Look at the climate graph below and answer the following questions.

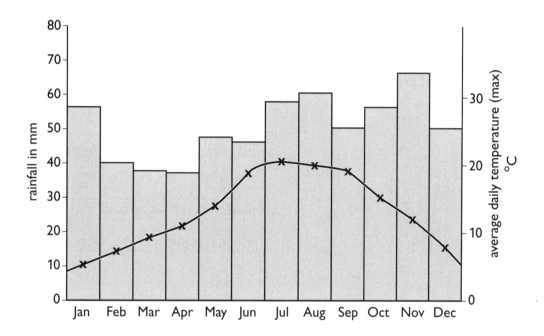

(a) In which month is the highest temperature? (1)

(b) In which month is the lowest temperature? (1)

(c) Which month has the highest rainfall? (1)

(d) What is the range of temperature? (1)

(e) How would you expect the climate of the north-west of the British Isles to differ from the climate shown on this graph and why? (6)

2.15 Draw a well-labelled diagram of the water cycle.   (6)

2.16 What is the difference between evaporation and precipitation?   (2)

2.17 Select any **two** of the following and explain how they may affect local weather
       conditions.

       mountain   aspect   coast   forest   town   (6)

2.18 Explain the influence of the following on the British climate:

       (a) a location between 50 and 60 degrees north   (2)

       (b) the Gulf Stream (North Atlantic Drift)   (2)

2.19 The diagram below shows areas of the UK. Match the letters A–D to the
       climate description that best suits that area.   (4)

Climate description

| mild summers, mild winters and wet |

| warm summers, cold winters and dry |

| mild summers, very cold winters and dry |

| warm summers, mild winters and wet |

Letter	Climate description
A	
B	
C	
D	

2.20 Look at the map below which shows six different locations in the grounds of a school.

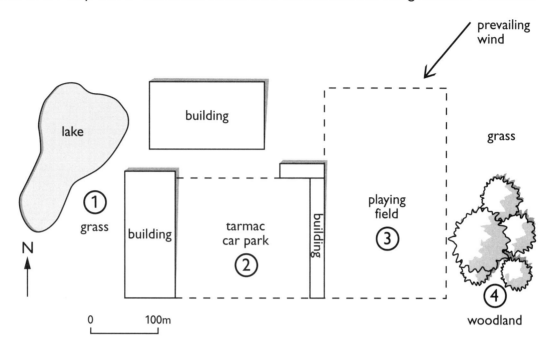

(a) Which is the best location for a Stevenson screen? Why? (3)

(b) Which location will have the highest temperature during the day? Why? (3)

2.21 Describe **three** processes in the water cycle. (3)

2.22 Draw a well-labelled diagram to explain how the mountains and the prevailing winds cause the west of Britain to be wetter than the east. Marks will be given for specific names of places, mountains and seas. (6)

2.23 Look at the table of climate data below and answer the following questions.

	J	F	M	A	M	J	J	A	S	O	N	D
Norwich average temp °C	7	7	10	14	16	19	21	20	19	15	10	7
Norwich total rainfall mm	60	50	40	50	40	40	65	50	55	55	65	60
Manchester average temp °C	9	9	10	12	15	18	20	20	17	12	10	8
Manchester total rainfall mm	80	60	50	55	60	55	80	90	75	90	80	55
Plymouth average temp °C	9	9	11	13	15	18	19	19	18	15	12	10
Plymouth total rainfall mm	120	75	70	55	55	50	60	75	75	90	115	115
Fort William average temp °C	4	4	10	11	15	16	17	17	15	12	10	5
Fort William total rainfall mm	250	175	125	125	100	110	130	150	175	225	190	220

(a) Which place has the highest annual rainfall? Why?   (2)

(b) What is the annual rainfall figure for the place with the highest rainfall?   (1)

(c) Which place has the highest temperature in summer? Why?   (2)

(d) Which place has the highest temperature in winter? Why?   (2)

(e) Which place has the lowest temperature in summer? Why?   (2)

(f) Which place experiences the rain shadow effect?   (1)

2.24   The map below shows January temperatures and snow cover.

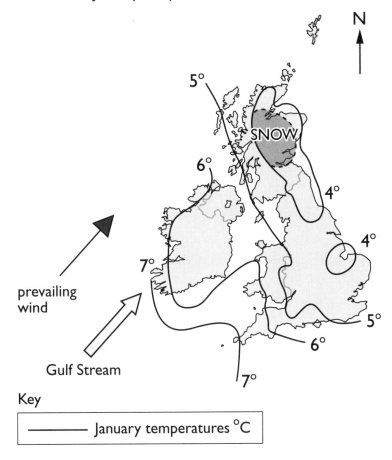

Key

——————— January temperatures °C

(a)   Why is snow most likely to be found in the area shown on the map?   (2)

(b)   What does the thick arrow in the south west corner of the map represent?   (1)

(c)   How would the isotherms (lines linking places of equal temperature) differ if the map was showing July temperatures? Why would the isotherms change shape?   (2)

2.25   List **three** stores in the water cycle.   (3)

2.26   How does distance from the sea affect temperature?   (2)

2.27   Why are places closer to the Equator hotter than places further away from the Equator?   (2)

2.28   Apart from latitude and proximity to the sea, name one other factor that affects temperature and explain how it influences temperature.   (2)

2.29   Why are urban areas hotter than rural areas?   (2)

2.30 Copy the table below and match the places to the types of rainfall they are most likely to receive. (3)

| London | Ben Nevis | the whole of the UK |

Type of rainfall	Place
relief rainfall	
frontal rainfall	
convectional rainfall	

3. Plate tectonics

3.1 Which option best completes each of the following sentences?

(a) Volcanoes can be found at .... (1)

conservative boundaries
destructive boundaries only
destructive and constructive boundaries
collision and constructive boundaries

(b) A destructive plate boundary occurs when .... (1)

two continental plates meet
two oceanic plates meet
plates move towards each other
plates move away from each other

(c) When an oceanic plate sinks under a continental plate .... (1)

a destructive plate boundary is formed
a constructive plate boundary is formed
a collision plate boundary is formed
a conservative plate boundary is formed

(d) When two oceanic plates move away from each other .... (1)

| a constructive boundary is formed | a collision boundary is formed |
| a destructive boundary is formed | a conservative boundary is formed |

(e) At destructive plate boundaries .... (1)

only volcanoes are formed
volcanoes and earthquakes are formed
earthquakes can happen but not volcanoes
ocean ridges are formed

(f) A subduction zone forms at a .... (1)

| destructive plate boundary | constructive plate boundary |
| collision plate boundary | conservative plate boundary |

3.2 Copy and complete the following sentences by choosing the correct word from the box below.

occur	heavier	conservative	do not occur	constructive
trenches	lighter	fold mountains		

(a) Volcanoes .... at plate boundaries. (1)

(b) Continental plates are .... than oceanic ones. (1)

(c) When two continental plates collide, ... are formed. (1)

(d) Earthquakes are likely to occur at .... plate boundaries, when plates rub together. (1)

3.3 Look at the map below that shows the distribution of the world's earthquakes and volcanoes.

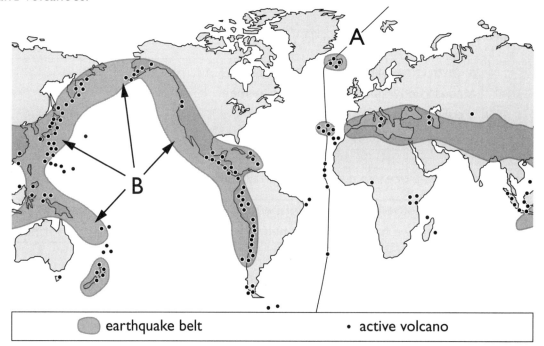

earthquake belt   • active volcano

(a) Describe the distribution of the earthquakes and volcanoes. (4)

(b) (i) What do geographers call area A? (1)

    (ii) What do geographers call area B? (1)

(c) Explain why volcanoes and earthquakes only occur in certain areas. (5)

3.4   Copy and complete the following sentences by choosing the correct words from the box below.

magma	lava	liquid	solid	convection currents
continental drift	ocean trench	focus	destructive	
constructive	collision	seismmometer	barometer	

(a)   The area of deep sea water where the oceanic plate subducts under the continental plate is known as the . . . . (1)

(b)   A subduction zone is found in a . . . . plate boundary.   (1)

(c)   Molten rock found under the Earth's crust is known as . . . . (1)

(d)   The mantle is made of . . . . rock.   (1)

(e)   A . . . . is used to measure the power of earthquakes.   (1)

(f)   The movement of magma in the mantle is known as . . . . (1)

3.5   (a)   Name a volcanic eruption you have studied and describe where it is located in the world.   (2)

(b)   Explain in detail why this volcanic eruption occurred.
(You could use an annotated diagram to do this.)   (5)

(c)   Describe how humans were affected by the eruption.   (4)

(d)   Describe how the environment was affected by the eruption.   (4)

3.6   Explain why people in LEDCs suffer more from the effects of volcanoes and earthquakes than people in MEDCs.   (4)

3.7   Define the following terms:

(a)   tectonic plate   (1)

(b)   tsunami   (1)

(c)   seismic wave   (1)

(d)   epicentre   (1)

3.8   Why do people live in areas that are prone to earthquakes and volcanoes?   (4)

3.9   (a) The diagram below shows a destructive plate boundary. Copy the diagram and label it using the words below.   (4)

Nazca plate (oceanic)	South American plate (continental)	
subduction zone	mantle	fold mountains
focus	epicentre	ocean trench

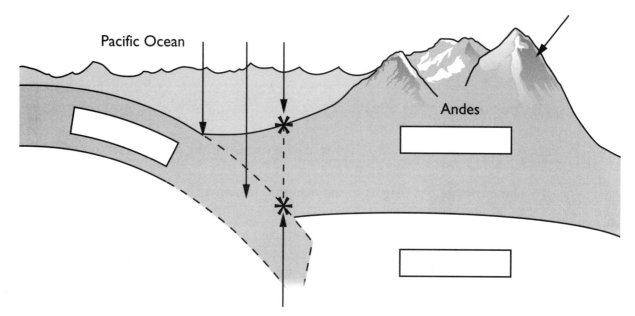

Pacific Ocean

Andes

(b) Add arrows to show the direction of movement of the plates.   (2)

3.10   What can humans do to try to lessen the damage and loss of life caused by volcanoes and earthquakes? Use specific examples in your answer.   (4)

3.11   Outline the problems faced by people who live near the Pacific Ring of Fire.   (4)

3.12   The table below shows information about some major earthquakes.

Date	Location	Richter Scale	Deaths
Dec 2004	S E Asia	8.9	300 000
Oct 1989	California, USA	7.1	63
Jan 2010	Hiati	7.0	210 000
Sep 1985	Mexico City	8.1	30 000

Why does the level of damage and the number of deaths caused by an earthquake vary so much?   (3)

3.13   The map below shows plate movement around Italy.

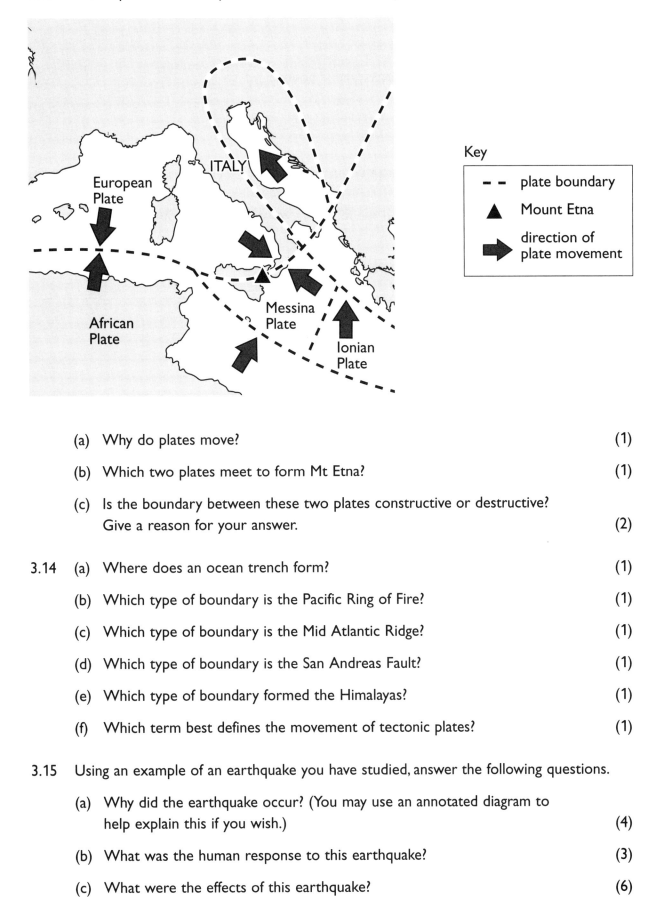

Key

- - -   plate boundary

▲   Mount Etna

➡   direction of plate movement

(a) Why do plates move?   (1)

(b) Which two plates meet to form Mt Etna?   (1)

(c) Is the boundary between these two plates constructive or destructive?
     Give a reason for your answer.   (2)

3.14 (a) Where does an ocean trench form?   (1)

     (b) Which type of boundary is the Pacific Ring of Fire?   (1)

     (c) Which type of boundary is the Mid Atlantic Ridge?   (1)

     (d) Which type of boundary is the San Andreas Fault?   (1)

     (e) Which type of boundary formed the Himalayas?   (1)

     (f) Which term best defines the movement of tectonic plates?   (1)

3.15 Using an example of an earthquake you have studied, answer the following questions.

     (a) Why did the earthquake occur? (You may use an annotated diagram to
          help explain this if you wish.)   (4)

     (b) What was the human response to this earthquake?   (3)

     (c) What were the effects of this earthquake?   (6)

3.16 For each of the following, state whether it is a **cause** or an **effect** of volcanoes and earthquakes.

    (a) Two continental plates collide. (1)

    (b) Plates lock together at a conservative boundary. (1)

    (c) A tsunami occurs. (1)

    (d) People are evacuated. (1)

    (e) Cheap geothermal energy can be produced. (1)

3.17 Copy the table below and match the following words to the appropriate type of volcano. (3)

extinct	active	dormant

a volcano which will never erupt again	
a volcano which could erupt but has not erupted recently	
a volcano which is erupting or showing signs of activity	

3.18 How do the human responses differ when a natural disaster such as a volcanic eruption or an earthquake occurs in an LEDC or an MEDC? (3)

3.19 Copy and complete the following paragraph using some of the words from the box below. (10)

mantle	Pangea	focus	rind	volcanoes
magma	outer core	plate boundary	inner core	crust
plates	convection currents	continental drift		
molten	earthquakes	floods		

The Earth is made up of layers. The centre of the Earth is known as the . . . .

Outside of this layer is the outer core. Around this is the . . . . which is

made up of molten . . . . This liquid rock is continuously moving as

. . . . The outermost layer is called the . . . .

This is broken into . . . . which gradually move due to the magma

moving beneath them. This movement of plates is known as . . . .

The place where two or more plates meet is known as a . . . . At these

places . . . . and . . . . can occur.

3.20 What is the difference between the focus and the epicentre of an earthquake? (2)

4. Economic geography

4.1 Which option best completes each of the following sentences?

(a) Agriculture is a . . . . (1)

primary industry	secondary industry
tertiary industry	quaternary industry

(b) Tourism is a . . . . (1)

primary industry	secondary industry
tertiary industry	quaternary industry

(c) A doctor works in a . . . . (1)

primary industry	secondary industry
service industry	manufacturing industry

(d) A manufacturing industry is a . . . . (1)

primary industry	secondary industry
tertiary industry	quaternary industry

(e) A carpenter works in a . . . . (1)

primary industry	secondary industry
tertiary industry	quaternary industry

(f) A tertiary industry . . . . (1)

is a manufacturing industry	is a service industry
involves research and development	is a mining industry

4.2 The following table shows the employment structure in two countries.

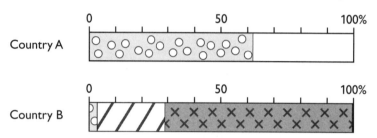

Key				
Economic sector	**Primary**	**Secondary**	**Tertiary**	**Quaternary**
Country A	62	11	27	0
Country B	3	26	70.5	0.5

(a) Copy and complete bar chart for country A using the information from the table. (2)

```
        0                    50              100%
        ├──┬──┬──┬──┬──┬──┬──┬──┬──┬──┬──┤
Country A │ ○ ○○ ○ ○ ○○ ○ │              │
        └──────────────────┴───────────────┘

        0                    50              100%
        ├──┬──┬──┬──┬──┬──┬──┬──┬──┬──┬──┤
Country B │/////│× × × × × × × × × × × ×│
        └─────┴────────────────────────────┘
```

(b) Which bar chart do you think represents a more developed country and which represents a less developed country? (2)

(c) Describe the differences in the employment structures of the two countries. (3)

(d) Explain the differences in the employment structures of the two countries. (3)

4.3 Define the following:

(a) primary industry (1)

(b) quaternary industry (1)

(c) NIC (1)

4.4 (a) The diagram below shows location factors for factories. Choose **three** of these location factors and explain why they are important. (6)

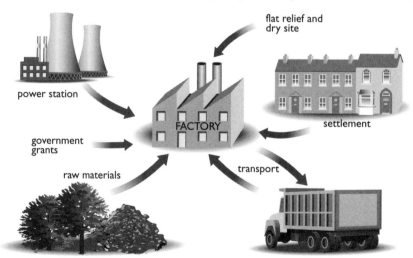

(b) Now choose **two** location factors and explain why they are not as important now as they were 100 years ago. (4)

4.5 On the OS map on the inside back cover look at the secondary industry (wks) in grid square 2985 and the industrial estate (Ind Est) in grid square 2786.

(a) Describe how their locations differ. (3)

(b) Which location do you think is more suitable for factories and why? (4)

4.6 Look at the OS map on the inside back cover. Copy and complete the table below giving examples of different industry types with their grid references. (6)

	Example	Grid reference
primary		
seconday		
tertiary		

4.7 (a) What type (sector) of economic activity is mining (quarrying)? (1)

(b) In grid square 2087, on the OS map on the inside back cover what conflicts might the opencast workings (quarry) cause in the local community? (4)

(c) Many of the quarries in this area have closed down. What impact will this have had on the area? (4)

(d) What is the main economic activity in this area? Use map evidence to support your answer. (2)

4.8 Copy and complete the table below by placing the following economic activities in the correct position. (7)

arable farming   **forestry**   **law**   **tourism**   **R&D**
entertainment   **cement works**

Primary	Secondary	Tertiary	Quaternary

4.9 For an economic activity you have studied:

    (a) Name it and describe its location. (2)

    (b) Give three factors that influence its location. (3)

    (c) Explain the reasons for **either** this industry's growth **or** decline in recent years. (3)

    (d) What has been the impact on the people in the local area of this industrial change? (3)

4.10 (a) Describe how the employment structure (percentage of people working in each sector) in the UK today is different from the structure in the 19th century. (3)

    (b) Explain why the employment structure has changed. (3)

4.11 The advertising board below shows the benefits of locating a company in a business park. Choose **four** of the attractions and explain why they would be beneficial to a new business. (4)

4.12 For an economic activity you have studied:

    (a) Describe its inputs, throughputs (processes) and outputs. (6)

    (b) Describe any linkages the activity may have. (2)

    (c) Explain the potential benefits and problems the industry may bring to the local area. (4)

4.13 Consider an example of an industry in your local area and an industry in an LEDC. Describe three differences between the working conditions for employees in the different industries. (3)

4.14   Copy and complete the following paragraphs using some of the words from
        the box below.   (13)

primary	farmers	secondary	LEDCs	MEDCs	urban
tertiary	primary	fishermen	develop	tertiary	large
quaternary	rural	lawyers	doctors	time	

. . . . industry involves the growing or extracting of raw material on or

from the Earth. In LEDCs a . . . . proportion of the population works in

this sector. Many people are subsistence . . . . Once a country begins to

. . . . , the number of people working in . . . .

industries will increase. However, most of these people will be working in factories run and

owned by . . . .

In MEDCs the majority of people work in . . . . industries, especially in

. . . . areas. A very small proportion of the population is involved in

. . . . industries which are concerned with research and development.

The employment structure of a country or region changes over . . . .

Two hundred years ago far fewer people in the UK worked in . . . .

industries and far more worked in . . . . industries as farmers, miners or

. . . .

5. Environmental geography

5.1   Which option matches each of the following definitions?

(a)   Using resources in a way that prevents them from running out.   (1)

sustainable development	preventative development
symbiotic development	social development

(b)   Low impact tourism aimed at protecting the natural environment and local cultures.   (1)

enviro-tourism	eco-tourism
brown tourism	fair tourism

(c)   Land that has not been built on before.   (1)

retail site	brownfield site
dormant site	greenfield site

(d)   A road built around a town.   (1)

through road	cul de sac
by-pass	lay-by

5.2   Look at the photo below.

(a)   What is the benefit of preserving this area?   (3)

(b)   Give reasons why there could be pressure to develop an area like this. Which groups of people may want to do this?   (4)

(c)   What could be done to try to stop development happening?   (1)

5.3 Referring to a 'managed' location you have studied, explain how the management plans have affected different groups of people in this area. Remember to include both positive and negative effects. (8)

5.4 What are the reasons for creating managed locations such as National Parks or nature reserves? (3)

5.5 Explain what the following terms mean:

(a) stewardship (1)

(b) exploit (1)

5.6 The percentages below show the land ownership in National Parks in England and Wales.

Individual private landowners	73%
National Trust	7%
Forestry Commission	6%
Water companies	5%
Ministry of Defence (MOD)	4%
National Park Authority (NPA)	2%
Nature Conservancy	2%
Other	1%

(a) On a copy of the pie chart below correctly shade the blank areas. (3)

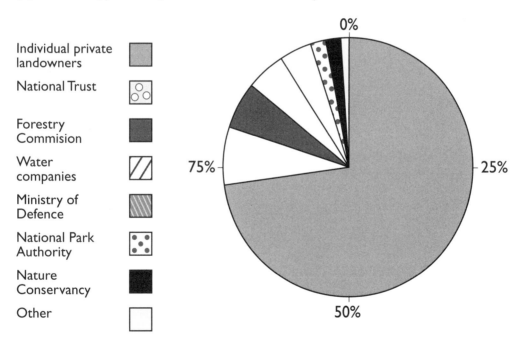

(b) Using the information on the graph and other ideas, explain why it is sometimes difficult to manage areas such as National Parks. (5)

5.7 For a particular location you have studied:

(a) Describe the human and physical features of this area that make it worth protecting. (4)

(b) Give **two** examples of land use conflict in this area. (2)

(c) Explain how and why people have tried to develop the area sustainably. (6)

5.8 Look at the map below.

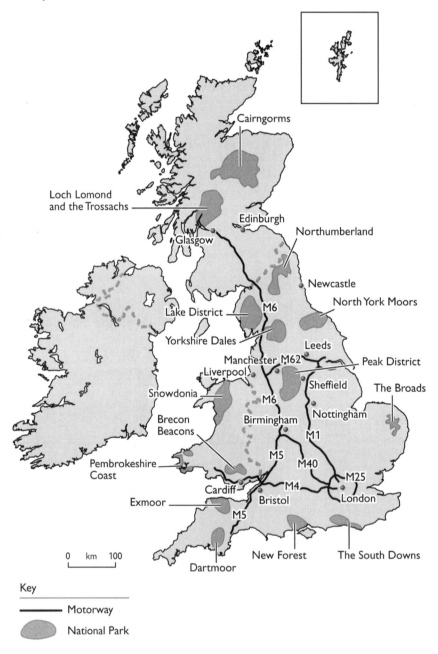

Key

———— Motorway

National Park

(a) Suggest which National Park is likely to be the most visited. (1)

(b) Why do you think this is? (2)

(c) What advantages and disadvantages can visitors bring to areas such as National Parks? (6)

5.9   The illustration below shows some of the problems caused by agriculture and tourism in some National Parks.

(a) Describe **one** way in which farmers may conflict with tourists.   (1)

(b) Describe **three** problems caused by tourists in an Area of Outstanding Natural Beauty, for example a National Park.   (3)

(c) Quarrying takes place in some National Parks. Describe the conflicts this may cause.   (3)

5.10   Look at the OS map on the inside back cover. This area is not a National Park.

(a) For what reasons do you think it is not a National Park?   (2)

(b) What physical features does this area contain which may make it worth conserving?   (3)

(c) Look at the woodland in grid square 2688. Why might this habitat be under threat?   (1)

5.11   Look at the OS map on the inside back. The local council is thinking of building an offshore wind farm in grid square 3185. What benefits and problems could this bring? (4)

5.12   The following land uses could be found close to each other:

| nature reserve | caravan site | Ministry of Defence firing range |

Describe the conflicts that could occur between any **two** of these land uses.   (3)

5.13   Look at the OS map on the inside back cover. If an out of town supermarket was built on the edge of Ashington in grid square 2586 what conflicts could arise?   (4)

5.14 (a) What do you understand by the word 'conservation'? (1)

(b) Give one example of conservation. (1)

5.15 Conservation and sustainable development do not only happen in MEDCs; National Parks have been set up in LEDCs.

(a) Explain why you think this has occurred. (3)

(b) What problems could occur for people who live inside these National Parks? (3)

5.16 Look at the aluminium works in grid square 2989 on the OS map on the inside back cover and explain what effect this factory may have on the human and physical environment. (3)

6. Global location

This section contains questions and maps to practice global location knowledge.

6.1   Look at Map 1 of Europe on the opposite page.

(a)   Members of a family are planning a holiday in Europe. On a copy of the map
      mark the following places they decide to visit: (4)

      Madrid   Berlin   Athens   Rome

(b)   Using part (a) to help you, label on the map **two** countries they will visit by
      following the chosen route.   (2)

(c)   On the holiday they will hike in the mountains marked **A** on the map.
      Name these mountains.   (1)

(d)   They will arrive in France to start their trip by crossing the English Channel.
      Mark and name this on your copy of the map.   (1)

(e)   Name the river marked on the map.   (1)

(f)   Mark the following on your map: (2)

      the Prime Meridian   the Pyrenees

Map 1

A

0   km   500

6.2 Look at Map 2 of North and South America on the opposite page.

A cruise took place along the east coast of the USA, then south to Tierra del Fuego, then up the west coast of South America and finally along the west coast of the USA.

(a) The cruise started in New York. Label this city on your copy of the map. (1)

(b) The ship then docked in the Gulf of Mexico and the passengers took a trip to Mexico City. Label this city on your map. (1)

(c) When they returned to the boat they then sailed south to the mouth of the Amazon River. Label this river on your map. (1)

(d) They then sailed around the coast of Brazil. Label this country on your map. (1)

(e) What is the capital city of Brazil? (1)

(f) Having sailed around Cape Horn, the passengers then had some amazing views of the Andes. Outline and label these mountains on your map. (1)

(g) What is the name of the ocean in which the boat is now sailing? (1)

(h) While heading even further north the passengers noticed some mountains in the distance on the west coast of the USA. What is the name of these mountains? (1)

(i) Finally the cruise ended on the west coast of Canada. Label this country on the map. (1)

(j) Some of the passengers finished off the trip of a lifetime with a canoe ride down the Mississippi. Label this river on the map. (1)

Map 2

12

6.3   Look at Map 3 of Europe and Africa on the opposite page.

(a)   What is the name of the LEDC marked **A** on the map?   (1)

(b)   What is the name of the MEDC marked **B** on the map?   (1)

(c)   What is the name of the capital city of country B?   (1)

(d)   When aid is sent to country **A**, the ship's route often follows the river whose mouth is in Egypt. What is the name of this river?   (1)

(e)   Organisations such as UNICEF often help country **A**. They fly their aid from Britain to country **A**. The plane refuels at the city marked **C** on the map. Name this city.   (1)

(f)   Name the ocean marked **D** and the ocean marked **E**.   (2)

(g)   Outline and label the Sahara Desert.   (1)

(h)   If you were flying from country **A** to Britain would you put your watch forward or back?   (1)

Map 3

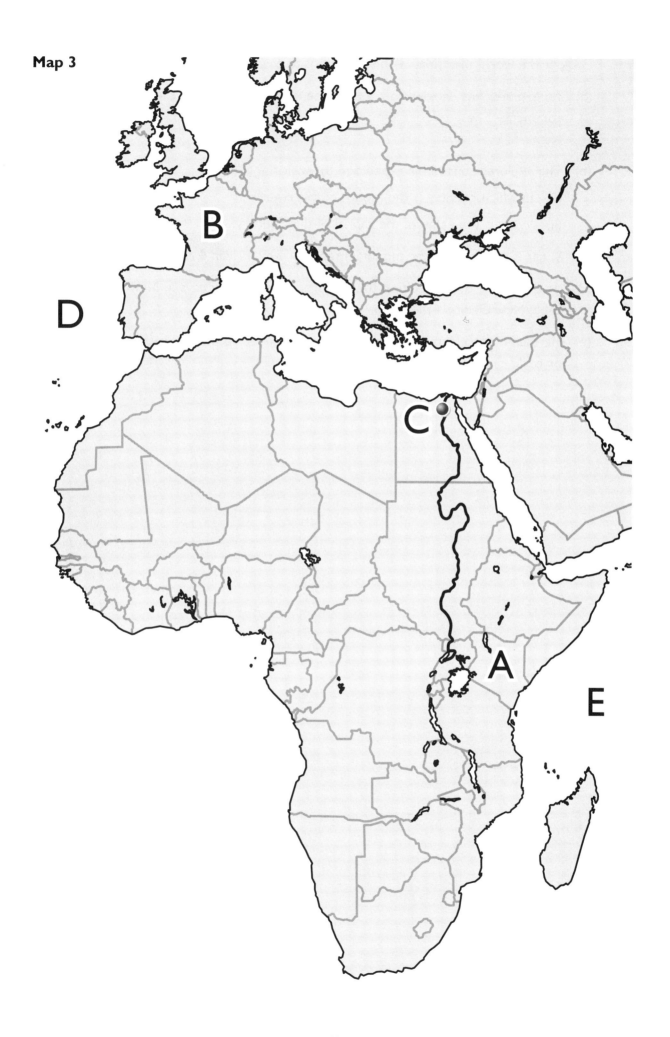

B

D

C

A

E

43

13

6.4 Look at the world map (Map 4) on the opposite page and answer these questions.

(a) An explorer has decided to try to canoe up a river in five of the world's continents. These rivers are marked **1** to **5** on the world map.
Name all five rivers. (5)

(b) The explorer started his expedition by exploring river **3**.

    (i) In which country is the mouth of this river? (1)

    (ii) What is the name of the capital of this country? (1)

(c) What is the name of the mountain range in which river **4** rises? (1)

(d) At the end of the expedition the explorer spends a few days in New Delhi.
Label New Delhi on the map. (1)

(e) He then flies to Ukraine for a week. Does he need to put his watch forward or back? (1)

Map 4

6.5 Look at the map of the world (Map 5) on the opposite page and answer the following questions.

(a) The Olympic Games in 2000 were held in Sydney, Australia. On a copy of the map, label Sydney. (1)

(b) On your map name the country marked **A** where many of the gold medallists came from. (1)

(c) If a British competitor telephoned from Sydney at 5pm, would it be morning or afternoon for the person answering the call in the UK? (1)

(d) In December what season is it in Sydney? (1)

(e) Other medallists came from the countries marked **B, C** and **D** on the map. Name these countries. (3)

(f) Name the mountains marked **E** where the British team carried out some of its training. (1)

(g) The Indian Olympic team flew from Delhi to Sydney. On the way they flew over **F, G** and **H**. Identify:

   (i)   **F** the line of latitude (1)

   (ii) **G** the country (1)

   (iii) **H** the line of latitude (1)

(h) The next Olympics in 2004 were held in Greece. What is the capital of Greece? (1)

Map 5

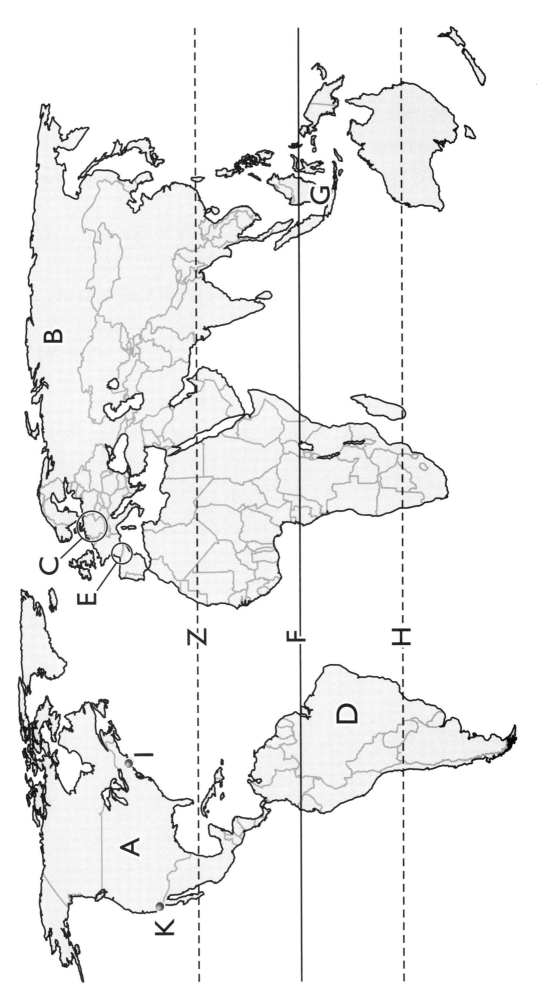

6.6 Look at Map 5 shown again on the opposite page. You have been invited to go on a hockey tour of the USA.

(a) Before the training programme, you fly to Paris for some extra training. On a new copy of the map label this city. (1)

(b) Paris is the capital of which country? (1)

(c) You then fly to London for a few days' rest. Over which stretch of water will you fly? (1)

(d) The coach comes from Kenya. Label this country on the map. (1)

(e) On which line of latitude does Kenya lie? (1)

(f) The first match is to be played in New York. Which letter marks where New York is on the map? (1)

(g) The second match is to be played in Los Angeles. Which letter marks where Los Angeles is on the map? (1)

(h) What is the name of the line of latitude marked **Z** on the map? (1)

(i) When you fly back from the USA to the UK, over which ocean will you pass? (1)

Map 5

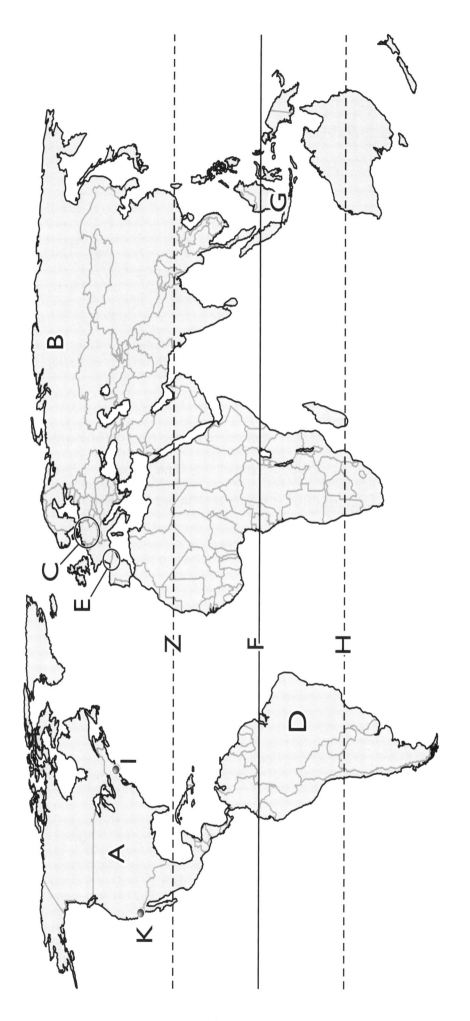

49

15 6.7 Look at the map of Europe (Map 6) on the opposite page and answer the following questions.

    (a) Name the cities marked with the following letters: **A**, **B**, **C** and **D**. (4)

    (b) Name countries **E** and **F**. (2)

    (c) On a copy of the map mark the following:

        the Alps
        the Pyrenees
        the Grampian mountains (3)

    (d) What is the capital city of the following countries?

        (i) Irish Republic (1)

        (ii) Germany (1)

        (iii) Greece (1)

        (iv) Russia (1)

        (v) Poland (1)

    (e) On your copy of the map label the following seas, oceans and rivers.

        Arctic Ocean   English Channel   The Rhine   River Severn (4)

    (f) Name the countries that make up the United Kingdom. (4)

Map 6

6.8   Look at the world map (Map 7) on the opposite page and answer the following questions.

Around the world there are many natural and man-made hazards as well as areas of conflict.

(a)   Name country **A**, which suffers regularly from flooding.   (1)

(b)   The flooding is partly caused by deforestation in the Himalayas. On a copy of the map outline and label these mountains.   (1)

(c)   Earthquakes can occur in Pakistan. Label this country on the map.   (1)

(d)   What is the name of the river marked **B**?   (1)

(e)   Indonesia can suffer from tropical cyclones. On your copy of the map outline the islands that make up this country and label the country.   (1)

(f)   Japan is on the Pacific Ring of Fire and suffers from volcanoes and earthquakes. What is the capital of this country?   (1)

(g)   India is a country that suffered in the Boxing Day tsunami in 2004. Label this country on your map.   (1)

(h)   Over the past decade there has been much war in the two countries labelled **C** and **D**. Name these two countries.   (2)

(i)   Name the line of latitude shown on the map. At what degree of latitude does this line lie?   (2)

Map 7

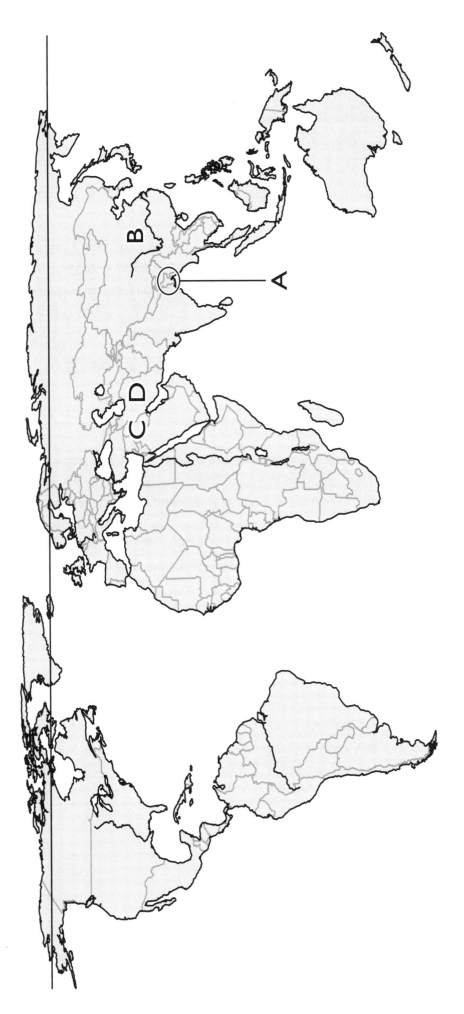

7. Fieldwork

Fieldwork investigations form an important part of the process of learning geographical skills. The fieldwork section of the 13+ Common Entrance examination accounts for 20% of the mark. It enables you to demonstrate that you understand geographical skills which cannot be examined in the written papers, for example, graphical skills. It is also a great deal of fun!

It is useful to have completed some practice fieldwork investigations before you embark on this section of the book.

Your Geography teacher will probably have arranged some time away from the normal school day to collect the data for your project. Perhaps you were lucky enough to visit a field centre some distance from your school, or perhaps you went abroad, or collected data in your local area. It does not matter where you collect the data; what is important is that you collect the right data, listen carefully to advice and have an enquiring mind.

You may submit your project as bound A4 sheets or you may submit it electronically on the pro forma provided by the examination board.

When do I complete the investigation?

You will have a number of weeks in which to organise yourself and write up your fieldwork investigation after you have collected the data. The best tip is to get the majority, if not all, of it done while the data collection stage is fresh in your mind. Your geography teacher will give you good advice and it is really important that you act on this. You will be given a deadline for the completion of the whole investigation. Your teacher may also give you deadlines for each section of your project. You will probably complete this investigation at the end of Year 7 or the start of Year 8. If you are sitting Common Entrance in February, the deadline for submission of your project to your senior school is January; if you are sitting Common Entrance in the summer, then the deadline is March.

How do I plan my investigation?

You will probably plan your investigation with your class and teacher. You may all start with the same aims or question to be answered. Your questions may be in the format of a hypothesis – a statement that you 'test' and either 'accept' or 'reject' at the end of your project. The suggested word limit for your project is 1000 words. Part of the skill of writing a fieldwork investigation is being concise.

Structure of the investigation

Your investigation should be divided into distinct sections and will be examined as such.

Section 1.   Introduction and question to be answered

You should include:

- a clearly stated question to be answered or a hypothesis

- a reason why you think this is a suitable question to be asked

- a brief description of the area of investigation

- information on the topic

- your geographical aims: your hypothesis

- a prediction of the outcome based on present knowledge.

Section 2.   Study area and data collection method

You should include:

- A map of the area. A hand drawn map is a good idea. If you use one from a computer make sure you annotate it. All maps should include a title, key, scale and north arrow.

- A photo of the methods. Ensure this is annotated.

You must:

- explain why this area was chosen as a suitable area for the investigation to be carried out

- explain why you used the methods you did for collecting the data

- include justification for these methods.

Section 3.   Data presentation

You should include at least two different ways of collecting your data:

- appropriate and accurate charts, graphs, sketch sections and tables can be used

- marks will be awarded for innovative ways of presenting your data

- headings and labelling on everything is vital.

Section 4.   Explanation, conclusion and evaluation

For each graph, chart or table you must explain:

- any patterns that emerge

- any odd results (anomalies), with suggested reasons why they occurred.

You must also do the following:

- Answer the question, or confirm or reject the hypothesis, that you stated at the beginning of the project. Give the geographical reasons for this.

- Give the limitations of your project. Describe how you could improve what you did. Describe what may change your outcomes.

- List your references, covering all the resources that you used, including books, maps and software programmes.

Fieldwork tips

1.   Listen carefully to instructions and information from teachers.

2.   Ask questions on your field trip and be alert to your surroundings at all times.

3.   Make concise notes on your return to the field centre or your classroom while the details are still fresh in your mind.

4.   Neatness, punctuation, spelling and general presentation are all taken into account when your work is marked.

5.   All work should be presented on A4 paper or scanned onto the ISEB pro forma. Smaller or larger formats are not allowed. All maps, charts, etc must also be presented on A4. Do not include folding maps – it is better to photocopy the relevant area and insert it on A4 paper.

6.   Draw some of your graphs, pie charts, tables and sketches by hand to demonstrate you possess that skill. Contrast this by using the computer. The examiner is looking for a variety of presentation techniques.

7.   Use suitable coloured pencils when shading.

8.   Do not forget appropriate titles, keys, scale, direction and labelling.

9.   Always save your information on a memory stick and a hard drive!

10.   If in doubt about any aspect of your fieldwork investigation ask your teacher for clarification. However, it is your work only that will be marked.

11.   Deadlines are deadlines! A rushed job can be spotted a mile off.

12.   Be enthusiastic and put your skills, time and effort into your investigation and you will produce a piece of work of which you can be proud.

Who marks my investigation?

The investigation is moderated by your geography teachers and given a mark out of 20. A breakdown is shown below:

Data presentation	**4**
Explanation of geography	**6**
Quality of presentation	**5**
Effort	**5**

This mark out of 20 will become a percentage and be added to your written exam mark in June (or February).

This process takes a long time, as each individual investigation has to be thoroughly checked. Investigations or ISEB pro formae and assessment forms are sent to senior schools. On the assessment form your teacher is asked to include written information about the amount of assistance you have been given. Your teacher will be accurate and truthful when it comes to moderating and answering this question. You will also have to sign to state that it is you who has completed this work.

It is really important that you:

- show enthusiasm and commitment

- take advice

- ask teachers for guidance when relevant

- manage your time effectively and efficiently

- produce an investigation that shows your geographical skills in the best possible light.

Good luck to all!